Roll over
and other stories

Hannie Truijens

Nelson

Roll over

There were five in the bed
and little Deb said,
"Roll over, roll over."

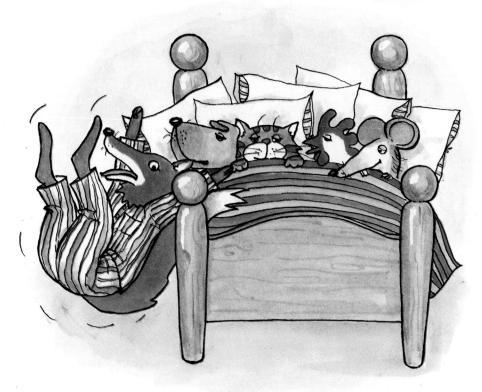

So they all rolled over and
Sam fell out.
There were four in the bed
and little Deb said,
"Roll over, roll over."

So they all rolled over and
Ben fell out.
There were three in the bed
and little Deb said,
"Roll over, roll over."

4

So they all rolled over and
Jip fell out.
There were two in the bed
and little Deb said,
"Roll over, roll over."

So they all rolled over and
Meg fell out.
There was one in the bed
and little Deb said,
"Goodnight."

Run rabbits run

One little rabbit sits in the
sun.
"If I had a friend it would be
fun."

Two little rabbits hop in the
sun.

"If we had a friend it would be
fun."

Three little rabbits skip in the sun.

"If we had a friend it would be fun."

Four little rabbits ride in the sun.

"If we had a friend it would be fun."

Five little rabbits play in the sun.

Here comes a fox.

Run rabbits run.

Five fat little fish

Five fat little fish in the
big blue sea.
"This looks good.
What can it be?"

12

Four fat little fish in the
big blue sea.
"This looks good.
What can it be?"

Three fat little fish in the
big blue sea.
"This looks good.
What can it be?"

Two fat little fish in the

big blue sea.

"This looks good.

What can it be?"

One fat little fish in the

big blue sea.

"This looks good.

But not for me."